JV.16

W9-BTP-631

3 5674 05817039 1

Lincoln Branch Library
1221 E. Seven Mile Road
Detroit, Michigan 48203
313-481-1782

APR 2019

© 2012, 2016 Age of Learning, Inc.
Published by Age of Learning, Inc., P.O. Box 10458, Glendale, California 91209.
No part of this work may be reproduced in whole or in part, or stored in a retrieval system,
or transmitted in any form or by any means, electronic, mechanical, photocopying,
recording, or otherwise, without written permission of the publisher.
ABCmouse.com and associated logos are trademarks and/or
registered trademarks of Age of Learning, Inc.

Library of Congress Cataloging-in-Publication Data
The Boy Who Cried Wolf/Age of Learning, Inc.
Summary: A young shepherd boy amuses himself by summoning the adults from
his village with false alarms, then learns the importance of honesty.

ISBN: 978-1-62116-000-7
Library of Congress Control Number: 2012912042

21 20 19 18 17 16 15 14 13 12   3 4 5
Printed in the U.S.A., on 10% recycled paper. ♻

The Boy who Cried Wolf

An Aesop's Fable

Age of Learning, Inc., Glendale, California
This book is also available at **ABCmouse.com**, the award-winning early learning online curriculum.

Aesop's Fables

What are Aesop's fables?

Legend tells us that Aesop lived a very long time ago in a place called Greece and became famous for telling stories that were intended to teach lessons about life. We call his stories Aesop's fables.

The Boy who Cried Wolf

Once there was a shepherd boy who tended the flock of sheep not far from his village. As a shepherd, his job was to make sure that the villagers' sheep were safe and didn't wander away.

One day, when the shepherd boy was feeling bored just watching the sheep graze, he decided to play a trick on the villagers to amuse himself.

He began yelling, "Wolf! Wolf!" as loud as he could, knowing that the villagers would come running to help protect him and the sheep.

Well, there was no wolf, of course. When the villagers arrived, the boy laughed at them. The villagers realized that they had been tricked and were angry at the boy.

But the boy thought that making the villagers stop what they were doing and come running was very funny. So he played the same trick on the villagers the next day, then again a few days later. Both times the villagers were very upset.

A few days later, as the boy was tending the sheep, a real wolf approached the flock. When the boy saw the wolf, he immediately yelled, "Wolf! Wolf!"

WOLF!
WOLF!

But this time no one came to help him. The villagers thought the boy was up to his old tricks, and they didn't want to be laughed at again. So they simply ignored his cries.

Sadly, this time it wasn't a trick. The boy was no match for the wolf, who easily stole the sheep.

From this, the shepherd boy learned two important lessons. First, you should never yell for help if you don't really need it. Second, if you tell lies, people won't believe you even when you're telling the truth.

The boy went to the villagers and apologized for how he had been acting and humbly asked for another chance. He promised he would never fail them again.

It took many months for everyone to trust him, but the shepherd boy had learned his lesson. Because of the shepherd boy's hard work, the wolf never stole another one of the villagers' sheep.

The End

Moral of the Story

Liars are not believed, even when they tell the truth.

Glossary

amuse Definition: If you **amuse** someone, you give them something to think about or to do that is interesting and fun. **Example:** One day, when the shepherd boy was feeling bored just watching the sheep graze, he decided to play a trick on the villagers to **amuse** himself.

approach Definition: If you **approach** something, you move closer to it. **Example:** A few days later, as the boy was tending the sheep, a real wolf **approached** the flock.

fable Definition: A **fable** is a short story that is intended to teach a lesson. **Example:** We call his stories Aesop's **fables**.

flock Definition: A **flock** is a group of sheep, goats, or birds that live together. **Example:** Once there was a shepherd boy who tended the **flock** of sheep not far from his village.

graze Definition: When animals **graze**, they eat grass and other plants. **Example:** One day, when the shepherd boy was feeling bored just watching the sheep **graze**, he decided to play a trick on the villagers to amuse himself.

Greece Definition: **Greece** is a country in Europe that has many islands, mountains, and beaches. It has existed for thousands of years. **Example:** Legend tells us that Aesop lived a very long time ago in a place called **Greece**.

ignore Definition: If you **ignore** something, you decide not to pay any attention to it. **Example:** The villagers thought the boy was up to his old tricks, and they didn't want to be laughed at again. So they simply **ignored** his cries.

immediately Definition: When something happens **immediately**, it happens right away without any waiting. **Example:** When the boy saw the wolf, he **immediately** yelled, "Wolf! Wolf!"

Glossary

intend **Definition:** When you **intend** to do something, you decide that's what you want to do. **Example:** Legend tells us that Aesop lived a very long time ago in a place called Greece and became famous for telling stories that were **intended** to teach lessons about life.

legend **Definition:** A **legend** is a story from long ago. Legends usually have events that could happen and other events that could not really happen. **Example:** **Legend** tells us that Aesop lived a very long time ago in a place called Greece.

lesson **Definition:** A **lesson** is something that a person is supposed to learn. **Example:** It took many months for everyone to trust him, but the shepherd boy had learned his **lesson**.

moral **Definition:** The **moral** of a story is the lesson the reader is supposed to learn from the story. **Example: Moral** of the story: Liars are not believed, even when they tell the truth.

realize **Definition:** If you **realize** something, you begin to understand or know something that you didn't know before. **Example:** The villagers **realized** that they had been tricked and were angry at the boy.

shepherd **Definition:** A **shepherd** is a person who takes care of sheep. **Example:** Once there was a **shepherd** boy who tended the flock of sheep not far from his village.

tend **Definition:** If you **tend** something or someone, you watch and take care of it or them. **Example:** Once there was a shepherd boy who **tended** the flock of sheep not far from his village.

wander **Definition:** If you **wander** away, you walk away from where you are without trying to go to any particular place. **Example:** As a shepherd, his job was to make sure that the villagers' sheep were safe and didn't **wander** away.

25

ABCmouse.com®
Early Learning Academy

CHILD SAFE · NO ADVERTISING · NO POP-UP ADS · NO EXTERNAL LINKS

Online Preschool • Pre-k
Kindergarten • 1st Grade • 2nd Grade

More than 8,500 Fun-Filled Learning Activities!

Award-winning Curriculum with Proven Results

Parents' Choice
GOLD Award

Teachers'
Choice Award

Teachers'
Choice Award
for the Classroom

Mom's Choice
Award GOLD

Editor's
Choice Award

The leading and most comprehensive
online learning resource for children ages 2–8+.

 **Reading**

 **Math**

 **Games**

 **Art & Colors**

 **World Around Us**

 **Music Videos**

 **Library**

 **My Aquarium**

 **Songs**

 **Zoo**

 **Farm**

 **Map**

"This website is amazing! My children are excited to learn and they don't want to stop. I'm so glad that I made the decision to invest in my children's education by signing up with ABCmouse.com. Thank you! I'm a happy mother! **"**

—Mother of 3- and 5-year-old girls

Learn more at
www.ABCmouse.com

Short Vowels

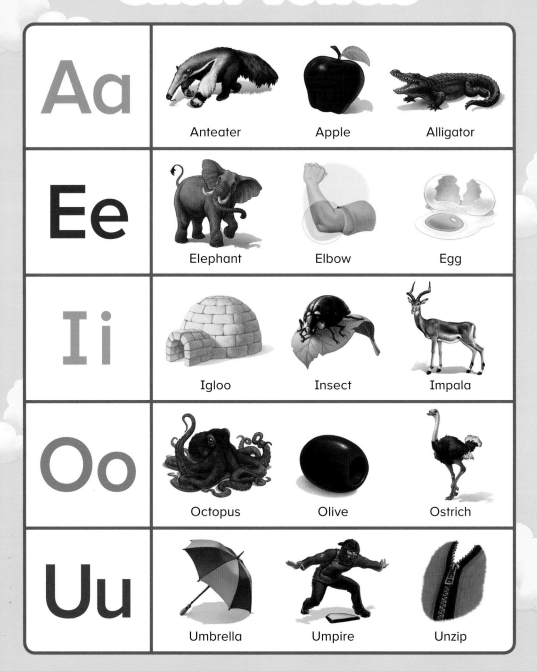

Aa	Anteater	Apple	Alligator
Ee	Elephant	Elbow	Egg
Ii	Igloo	Insect	Impala
Oo	Octopus	Olive	Ostrich
Uu	Umbrella	Umpire	Unzip

As you say the words for these items with your child, ask him or her to notice the first sound in each word. Explain that it is called the short (a, e, i, o, or u) sound.

Long Vowels

Aa	Apron	Acorn	April
Ee	Eagle	Easel	Eel
Ii	Ice Cream	Iron	Island
Oo	Ocean	Oval	Overalls
Uu	Unicorn	Unicycle	Ukulele

As you say the words for these items with your child, ask him or her to notice the first sound in each word. Explain that it is called the long (a, e, i, o, or u) sound.